A Fresh Approach
to Sight-Reading

Joining the Dots
for Guitar

Grade 1

Alan Bullard and Richard Wright

ABRSM

To the Teacher

Joining the Dots offers lots of material to help build skill and confidence in sight-reading. Used as part of regular lessons and practice, it will help students learn to read new music more quickly and easily, developing their awareness of fingerboard geography, their sense of key and other general musicianship skills.

The five books in the series cover the keys found in ABRSM's sight-reading tests at each of Grades 1–5, with a section for each key. Each section begins with warm-up and technical material ('Key Features' and 'Workouts'), followed by opportunities for improvisation ('Make Music') and several short pieces to sight-read ('Read and Play').

Key Features are a supplement to scales and arpeggios, and will help pupils to establish basic hand shapes and the 'feel' of each key under the fingers. They can be practised at various speeds and dynamics.

Workouts are for exercising and warming up the fingers and hands in the key, and explore a range of techniques. The first of each pair is the same throughout (transposed for each key), to help reinforce key familiarity, while the second is always different.

Make Music provides an opportunity for your pupils to build confidence in (and through) creative and imaginative work, and to develop aural skills. The activities here will also help to familiarize pupils with the 'feel' of the key, but using an approach that is not primarily notation-based. The first is always an 'echo' piece, which will help with listening skills and relate these to the fingerboard; the other two are more creative, and you and your pupils can approach these together in whatever way is most comfortable: for most pupils this will involve exploring the guitar with some trial and error – experimenting is a good way to learn here!

Read and Play is the goal of each section – a number of short, characterful pieces, to be played at sight or after a short practice time, with the focus on keeping going. These lead up to and include the technical standard to be found in Grade 1 sight-reading and are a useful source of sight-reading material for those preparing for exams. These pieces may occasionally be slightly longer than the pieces found in Grade 1 sight-reading.

Because the material is arranged to be at an equivalent level in each key, your pupils can 'jump in' to any section, using it alongside pieces, scales or arpeggios that are being learnt in that key. However, within each section it is recommended that pupils learn and play the Key Features and Workouts before moving on to the Make Music and Read and Play material.

Towards the end of the book you will find **More Pieces to Play**, including longer solo pieces, and some duets and trios suitable for group work. These can be used in any way you wish – as additional sight-reading practice or as pieces to learn quickly and play through for fun.

First published in 2012 by ABRSM (Publishing) Ltd, a wholly owned subsidiary of ABRSM, 24 Portland Place, London W1B 1LU, United Kingdom

© 2012 by The Associated Board of the Royal Schools of Music

AB 3672

Illustrations by Willie Ryan, www.illustrationweb.com/willieryan
Book design and cover by www.adamhaystudio.com
Music and text origination by Julia Bovee
Printed in England by Caligraving Ltd, Thetford, Norfolk

Dear Guitarist,

Joining the Dots will help you to learn new music more quickly and easily.

In this book you will find a section for each key that you are likely to use.

In each section there are several different things to do:

Key Features to get you used to playing in the key

Make Music in which you can develop and explore musical ideas

Workouts to exercise your fingers and hands

Read and Play where there are a number of short pieces to play – read the title, work out the rhythm, find the notes and, when you're ready, play the piece right through without stopping!

Towards the end of the book you'll find **More Pieces to Play**, including some longer pieces, and duets and trios to play with your friends.

Enjoy Joining the Dots!

Alan Bullard

Richard Wright

C major

Key Features

- Practise the first two bars in two ways, *tirando* and *apoyando*, always starting with the correct RH finger
- When you play these two bars *tirando*, rest the thumb on the G string

- For the first two bars, rest *i* and *m* on the G and B strings

Workouts

- Practise these workouts to warm up in the key of C major

- Start with *m* resting on the top E string, ready to take over from the thumb
- Make the staccatos in bar 2 by returning the thumb to the string as early as you can

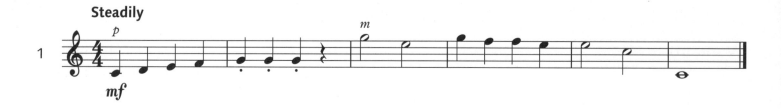

- Start with *p*, *i* and *m* ready on their strings, and place them again to make the rests at the end of bars 2 and 4

Make Music

Echoing Footsteps

- Make a tune with your teacher by echoing each phrase, in time
- Your teacher will show you which note to start on and count in two bars to set the pulse
- Don't look at the music or at your teacher's fingers – just listen

You can also try singing these echoes to 'la'.

My Cat

Make a tune to fit the words below:

- First of all, say the words out loud to make a rhythm
- Then turn the rhythm into a tune, using the first five notes of the C major scale, from C up to G
- Start and end on the note C – either the 2nd string C (using the RH fingers) or the 5th string C (using the thumb)

My black cat's called Daisy; she is very lazy.

You can sing along with the words while you play, if you like.

A Tune in Time

- Tap this rhythm several times
- When you can do it, make the rhythm into a tune (for either thumb or fingers), using the first five notes of the C major scale, from C up to G
- Start on any of these notes and finish on the note C

Happily

Read and Play

- Look at the time signature and count two bars of crotchets, out loud
- Keep counting, and tap the rhythm
- Then check the first note and the fingering
- If you like, try out the piece first
- Finally, play it right through without stopping!

For *On the Move* and *By the Lake* there's a duet part for your teacher.

On the Move

- Keep a steady beat in this march

By the Lake

- Create a peaceful mood here

• Remember to check the first note and get your fingers ready on the strings (both hands!)

Coming Down the Stairs

• Start with the thumb resting on the D string, ready for when its turn comes
• Aim for a smooth crescendo from beginning to end
• Count carefully and don't rush!

Knocking on the Door

• Make as much contrast as you can between the loud and quiet dynamics

Peaceful Thoughts

• Aim for a calm and gentle mood

Dancing Duet

• Here's a lively dance to play with a friend
• The second player plays the same music, beginning when the first player reaches the asterisk sign (✳)

Key Features

- Practise the first two bars in two ways, *tirando* and *apoyando*, always starting with the correct RH finger
- When you play these two bars *tirando*, rest the thumb on the D string

- For the first two bars, rest *i* and *m* on the G and B strings

Workouts

- Practise these workouts to warm up in the key of A minor

- Start with *m* resting on the top E string, ready to take over from the thumb
- Make the staccatos in bar 2 by returning the thumb to the string as early as you can

- The two-note slur means you should play the second note more quietly than the first
- If you play *tirando* with your fingers, start with the thumb resting on the D string

Make Music

A Minor Echo

- Make a tune with your teacher by echoing each phrase, in time
- Your teacher will show you which note to start on and count in two bars to set the pulse
- Don't look at the music or at your teacher's fingers – just listen

You can also try singing these echoes to 'la'.

Not Very Well!

Make a tune to fit the words below:

- First of all, say the words out loud to make a rhythm
- Then turn the rhythm into a tune, using the first five notes of the A minor scale, from A up to E
- Start and end on the 5th string A (using the thumb)
- Make it sound as if you are really fed up!

Feeling gloomy, stuck in bed, tired and bored with aching head!

You can sing along with the words while you play, if you like.

Marching By

- Tap this rhythm several times
- When you can do it, make the rhythm into a tune (for either thumb or fingers), using the first five notes of the A minor scale, from A up to E
- Start on any of these notes and finish on the note A

Rhythmic and steady

Read and Play

- Look at the time signature and count two bars of crotchets, out loud
- Keep counting, and tap the rhythm
- Then check the first note and the fingering
- If you like, try out the piece first
- Finally, play it right through without stopping!

   For **Cheerfully Minor** and **The End of the Day** there's a duet part for your teacher.

Cheerfully Minor

- Minor key music doesn't have to be sad – make this as happy as you can!

The End of the Day

- Imagine the sun setting slowly over the horizon

• Remember to check the first note and get your fingers ready on the strings (both hands!)

Cat and Mouse

• The slinky cat is played with the thumb, the scampering mouse with the fingers
• Start with *m* resting on the top E string

Question and Answer

• Play this piece as smoothly as you can
• If you play *tirando* with your fingers, start with the thumb resting on the D string

Fingers and Thumb

• Make this little conversation between fingers and thumb as rhythmic as you can

Minor March

• Here's a rhythmic march to play with a friend
• The second player plays the same music, beginning when the first player reaches the asterisk sign (✱)

G major

Key Features

- Practise the first two bars in two ways, *tirando* and *apoyando*, always starting with the correct RH finger
- When you play these two bars *tirando*, rest the thumb on the D string

- For the first two bars, rest *i* and *m* on the G and B strings

Workouts

- Practise these workouts to warm up in the key of G major

- Start with *m* resting on the B string, ready to take over from the thumb
- Make the staccatos in bar 2 by returning the thumb to the string as early as you can

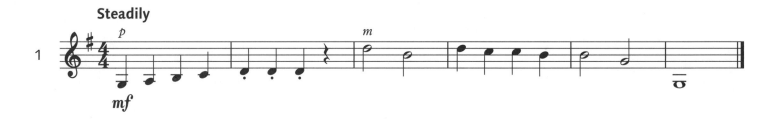

- Notice that each RH finger has its own string to play
- The two-note slur means you should play the second note more quietly than the first

Make Music

Nearly Home!

- Make a tune with your teacher by echoing each phrase, in time
- Your teacher will show you which note to start on and count in two bars to set the pulse
- Don't look at the music or at your teacher's fingers – just listen

You can also try singing these echoes to 'la'.

Window Shopping

Make a tune to fit the words below:

- First of all, say the words out loud to make a rhythm
- Then turn the rhythm into a tune, using the first five notes of the G major scale, from G up to D
- Start and end on the note G – either the 3rd string open G (using the RH fingers) or the 6th string G (using the thumb)

Walking down the high street, looking in the shops.

You can sing along with the words while you play, if you like.

Hopping

- Tap this rhythm several times
- When you can do it, make the rhythm into a tune (for either thumb or fingers), using the first five notes of the G major scale, from G up to D
- Start on any of these notes and finish on the note G

Andante

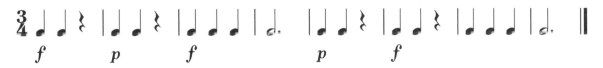

Read and Play

- Look at the time signature and count two bars of crotchets, out loud
- Keep counting, and tap the rhythm
- Then check the first note and the fingering
- If you like, try out the piece first
- Finally, play it right through without stopping!

For *On the River* and *Best Foot Forward* there's a duet part for your teacher.

On the River

- Think of a rowing boat floating gracefully down a river

Andante e legato

Best Foot Forward

- Imagine you are marching steadily along a road

Like a march

- Remember to check the first note and get your fingers ready on the strings (both hands!)

Cloudless Sky

- Create a calm mood with smooth and expressive playing – not too fast

Steadily

Bouncing Ball

- Bounce the ♫ ♩ rhythms between the fingers and thumb

Andante

Raindrops

- Suggest the drops of rain by playing this piece as neatly as you can

Delicately

Hill Walking

- Here's a piece to play with a friend – aim for a confident mood from the start
- The second player plays the same music, beginning when the first player reaches the asterisk sign (✲)

Andante

E minor

Key Features

- Practise the first two bars in two ways, *tirando* and *apoyando*, always starting with the correct RH finger
- When you play these two bars *tirando*, rest the thumb on the D string

- For the first two bars, rest *m* on the G string

Workouts

- Practise these workouts to warm up in the key of E minor

- Start with *m* resting on the B string, ready to take over from the thumb
- Make the staccatos in bar 2 by returning the thumb to the string as early as you can

- Both phrases should be played as legato as possible, and with an evenly matched sound
- If you play *tirando* with your fingers, start with the thumb resting on the D string

Make Music

Copycat

- Make a tune with your teacher by echoing each phrase, in time
- Your teacher will show you which note to start on and count in two bars to set the pulse
- Don't look at the music or at your teacher's fingers – just listen

You can also try singing these echoes to 'la'.

A Winter's Day

Make a tune to fit the words below:

- First of all, say the words out loud to make a rhythm
- Then turn the rhythm into a tune, using the first five notes of the E minor scale, from E up to B
- Start and end on the note E – either the 4th string E (using the RH fingers) or the 6th string E (using the thumb)

Footprints in the snowy ground, freezing frost is all around.

You can sing along with the words while you play, if you like.

A Sad Story

- Tap this rhythm several times
- When you can do it, make the rhythm into a tune (for either thumb or fingers), using the first five notes of the E minor scale, from E up to B
- Start on any of these notes and finish on the note E

Andante espressivo

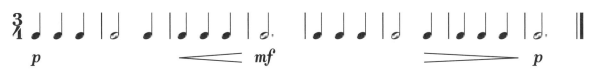

Read and Play

- Look at the time signature and count two bars of crotchets, out loud
- Keep counting, and tap the rhythm
- Then check the first note and the fingering
- If you like, try out the piece first
- Finally, play it right through without stopping!

For *Far from Home* and *Rocking Chair* there's a duet part for your teacher.

Far from Home

- Make this melody sad and expressive

Rocking Chair

- Imagine you are slowly and gently rocking backwards and forwards

• Remember to check the first note and get your fingers ready on the strings (both hands!)

Sarabande

• A sarabande is a slow and stately dance, which originally came from Spain
• If you play *tirando* with your fingers, start with the thumb resting on the D string

I'm Late!

• Play this piece as fast as you can, but don't let it run away with you – count carefully

Over the Stile

• Climb onto the stile, step over, and jump down the other side
• Start with *m* resting on the B string

Autumn Reflections

• Here's a gentle piece to play with a friend – make each phrase as smooth as you can
• The second player plays the same music, beginning when the first player reaches the asterisk sign (✳)

F major

Key Features

- Practise the first two bars in two ways, *tirando* and *apoyando*, always starting with the correct RH finger
- When you play these two bars *tirando*, rest the thumb on the D string

- For the first two bars, rest *m* on the G string

Workouts

- Practise these workouts to warm up in the key of F major

- Start with *m* resting on the B string, ready to take over from the thumb
- Make the staccatos in bar 2 by returning the thumb to the string as early as you can

- Aim for as much contrast as you can between the staccato and legato passages
- Make the staccatos with the RH, using the finger that is due to play next

Make Music

Echo Waltz

- Make a tune with your teacher by echoing each phrase, in time
- Your teacher will show you which note to start on and count in two bars to set the pulse
- Don't look at the music or at your teacher's fingers – just listen

Like a waltz

You can also try singing these echoes to 'la'.

Running for the Bus

Make a tune to fit the words below:

- First of all, say the words out loud to make a rhythm
- Then turn the rhythm into a tune, using the first five notes of the F major scale, from F up to C
- Start and end on the note F – either the 4th string F (using the RH fingers) or the 6th string F (using the thumb)

Running, running, running fast, running for the bus.

You can sing along with the words while you play, if you like.

Happy Hamster

- Tap this rhythm several times
- When you can do it, make the rhythm into a tune (for fingers), using the first five notes of the F major scale, from F up to C
- Start on any of these notes and finish on the note F

Allegretto

Read and Play

- Look at the time signature and count two bars of crotchets, out loud
- Keep counting, and tap the rhythm
- Then check the first note and the fingering
- If you like, try out the piece first
- Finally, play it right through without stopping!

For *Gently Dreaming* and *Folk Dance* there's a duet part for your teacher.

Gently Dreaming

- Make this melody gentle and relaxed

Folk Dance

- Play this lively dance twice
- Imagine that the dancers are in the distance the first time, and nearby the second time

• Remember to check the first note and get your fingers ready on the strings (both hands!)

Yachting

• Imagine a sailing boat drifting gently and smoothly in the breeze
• If you play *tirando* with your fingers, start with the thumb resting on the D string

Slow and calm

Surprise!

• Make the loud minims really sudden and unexpected!
• Start with *i* resting on the G string

Slowly

Calling Birds

• Imagine that two birds are singing to each other

Allegretto

Scaly Duet

• Here's a smooth and flowing piece to play with a friend
• The second player plays the same music, beginning when the first player reaches the asterisk sign (✱)

Andante

More Pieces to Play

- On the remaining pages you will find a variety of solo pieces of different lengths, and some duets and trios to play with your friends
- You can use these for playing at sight, or as pieces to learn on your own or with your teacher
- Don't forget to check the key signature and time signature, and to get the fingers of both hands in place on the strings before you start

Sunshine and Clouds

Grandly

Evening Calm

Allegretto espressivo

Nightfall

Moderato

Smooth and Solemn

Andante

Aiming High

Allegro

Snowdrifts

Slowly and smoothly

Up and Down

Confidently

Dripping Tap

Steadily

Looking Across the Lake

Andante

Eyes Closed

Dreamily

The Day Begins

With energy

More Pieces to Play

Butterflies

Dancing happily

Stealthy Approach

Moderate tempo

On the Swing

Energetically

Falling Leaves

I Agree!

Mighty Minuet

Blue Sky

Seaside Special

Trio in Three Keys

• When all the parts are played together, the effect is of the music moving gently from key to key

Night-Time March

Barbecue Bop